6. Pray for God's help. You *need* God's help in order to understand what you study in the Bible. PSALM 119:18 would be an appropriate verse for you to take to God in prayer.

7. *Class teachers using this course for group study will find some helpful suggestions on page 47.*

how to
take the self-check tests

Each lesson is covered by a test designed to help you evaluate what you have learned.

1. Review the lesson carefully in the light of the self-check test questions.

2. If there are any questions in the self-check test you cannot answer, perhaps you have written into your lesson the wrong answer from your Bible. Go over your work carefully to make sure you have filled in the blanks correctly.

3. When you think you are ready to take the self-check test, do so without looking up the answers.

4. Check your answers to the self-check test carefully with the answer key given on page 48.

5. If you have any questions wrong, your answer key will tell you where to find the correct answer in your lesson. Go back and locate the right answers. Learn by your mistakes!

apply
what you have learned
to your own life

In this connection, read carefully JAMES 1:22-25. It is only as you apply your lessons to your own life that you will really grow in grace and increase in the knowledge of God.

1

Introduction to Mark

Mark is preeminently the Gospel of service with the Lord Jesus Christ set forth as the servant obedient unto death (see PHILIPPIANS 2:7, 8). The servant character of the Lord Jesus is seen throughout the book and is clearly stated in 10:45. A particular emphasis is given to the miracles which the Lord Jesus performed, thus demonstrating His deity. Jesus is seen primarily as a Worker rather than as a Teacher.

Mark wrote primarily for the Gentiles who were not familiar with the Old Testament prophecies. Therefore, he uses only a few Old Testament references (1:2, 3; 14:27; 15:28). Mark is noted for its brevity and its vividness.

The author was a relative of Barnabas and a companion of Paul in his later ministry. The date of the Gospel is somewhere between A.D. 57 and 63.

Outline of Mark

God's Servant Presented

MARK 1

Chapter 1 tells of His baptism and temptation . . .

1. What is the general theme of the book?

MARK 1:1 _____

2. Under what titles did John the Baptist present Jesus?

JOHN 1:29, 34 _____

3. What prophecy had been recorded some 500 years before concerning the Messiah and His forerunner?

MALACHI 3:1 _____

4. What was the clear-cut message that John gave?

MARK 1:4 _____

5. What two actions are involved in true repentance?

PROVERBS 28:13 _____

6. Was there anything about the appearance of John that suggested earthly pomp?

MARK 1:6 _____

7. What place did he take in relation to Christ?

MARK 1:7 _____

8. Where was Jesus baptized?

MARK 1:9 _____

9. What three things happened when Jesus came up out of the water?

MARK 1:10, 11 _____

_____

10. Did Jesus confess any sins when He was baptized?

II CORINTHIANS 5:21 _____

11. Why did Jesus insist upon being baptized?

MATTHEW 3:14, 15 _____

In His case, it was not baptism "unto repentance" but "unto righteousness." To John, this occurrence was a sign that Jesus was the promised Messiah. To Jesus Himself it was His identification with sinners whom He had come to save.

12. What did the voice from heaven say?

MARK 1:11 _____

13. How is the Trinity of the Godhead seen in these verses?

MARK 1:10, 11 _____

_____

14. Where did Jesus immediately go after He was baptized?

MARK 1:12 _____

15. How long did the conflict with Satan last?

MARK 1:13 _____

16. What gospel did Jesus preach?

MARK 1:14 _____

17. What is this kingdom called in Matthew's account?

MATTHEW 4:17 _____

18. Did Jesus call idle men to be His followers?

MARK 1:16 _____

19. What kind of fishermen did He intend to make of them?

MARK 1:17 _____

20. Were these men willing to give up a good business to follow Jesus?

MARK 1:18-20 _____

The call of Christ should be superior to either parental claims or the claims of a prosperous business.

21. What was there in Jesus' manner that astonished the people?

MARK 1:22 _____

22. How should God's Word be taught today?

I PETER 4:11 _____

We never hear any real authority in Christian teaching apart from association with Christ as the Son of God and a profound belief in His Word.

23. What shows that the personality of the man in the synagogue was under the dominion of a foreign spirit?

MARK 1:23, 24 _____

24. Is it possible that one could recognize Jesus as the Son of God and still not be saved?

JAMES 2:19; MARK 5:1-9 _____

25. What did Jesus say that showed the man's testimony had the devil behind it?

MARK 1:25 _____

26. Did Jesus let the pressure of work interfere with prayer?

MARK 1:35 _____

27. Did the leper doubt the power of Jesus to heal, or His willingness?

MARK 1:40 _____

28. Should we put the "if" on Jesus, or on ourselves?

MARK 9:23 _____

29. What shows that Jesus did not want to be advertised among men as a wonder-worker?

MARK 1:44 _____

check-up time No. 1

You have just studied some important truths about the coming of the Lord Jesus. Review your study by rereading the Scripture lesson, the questions and your written answers. If you aren't sure of an answer, reread the Scripture portion given to see if you can find the answer. Then take the following test to see how well you understand the important truths you have studied. This exam covers lesson 1.

In the right-hand margin write "True" or "False" after each of the following statements.

1. The purpose of John's coming was to prepare the way for the Messiah. _____

2. John the Baptist presented Christ as the Good Shepherd. _____

3. Malachi gives a prophecy of the coming of John. _____

4. John considered himself to be greater than Jesus. _____

5. John said men must repent of their sins. _____

6. Jesus did have to confess sin. _____

7. Satan tried to keep the Lord Jesus from accomplishing His purpose in coming. _____

8. Jesus taught with authority because He is God. _____

9. Jesus' prayer life is an example to us. _____

10. Jesus worked miracles only to get the attention of the crowds. _____

Turn to page 48 and check your answers.

God's Servant Begins His Work

MARK 2 AND 3

Chapter 2 tells of the healing of the palsied man . . .

1. In this account whose faith did Jesus see?

MARK 2:4, 5 _____

2. What did Jesus see beneath this man's physical troubles?

MARK 2:5 _____

3. Did Jesus always lay sickness to a person's sins?

JOHN 9:3 _____

4. Why did the Pharisees deny Jesus the right to forgive sins?

MARK 2:7 _____

5. Why did Jesus have the authority to forgive sin?

JOHN 14:7-11 _____

6. How did Jesus prove that He was able to forgive sins?

MARK 2:10, 11 _____

7. What was Levi's name later changed to?

MATTHEW 9:9 _____

8. What was Levi's business?

MARK 2:14 _____

9. When the scribes and Pharisees had a complaint against Christ, to whom did they go?

MARK 2:16 _____

10. Whom did Jesus come to call?

MARK 2:17 _____

11. Are there any who are not sinners?

ROMANS 3:23 _____

12. How often did the Pharisees usually fast?

LUKE 18:11, 12 _____

13. Did Jesus believe fasting should be done regardless of circumstances?

MARK 2:19, 20 _____

14. What would happen if a piece of unshrunken new cloth were sewed onto a piece of old cloth?

MARK 2:21 _____

15. Did the disciples, according to the law, have the right to pluck corn on the Sabbath to satisfy hunger?

DEUTERONOMY 23:25 _____

16. Whom did Jesus use as an illustration to show that ceremonial observances must sometimes be set aside?

MARK 2:25, 26 _____

17. Who had full authority over the Sabbath?

MARK 2:27, 28 _____

Chapter 3 opens with the story of the man with the withered hand . . .

We may see in this incident a parable of service. We speak of one who does something skillfully as a "good hand." The hand is the organ for ministering, and when sin stops its usefulness it soon becomes paralyzed from inactivity.

18. What was the first thing Jesus required of the man?
MARK 3:3 _____

19. Why does the Lord likewise demand that we stand out before men in confession of Him?

ROMANS 10:9-11 _____

Jesus has no silent partners. We must step out upon His Word without being ashamed of our position before men.

20. Is it ever right to refuse to do good on any day of the week?

JAMES 4:17 _____

21. What was seen in Jesus' expression?

MARK 3:5 _____

Note that the only way to be angry and not sin is to be angry at nothing but sin.

22. What did Jesus tell the man to do?

MARK 3:5 _____

23. What was the result of this man's attempting the humanly impossible in obedience to Jesus' command?

MARK 3:5 _____

24. What two groups got together in their attempts to destroy Jesus?

MARK 3:6 _____

25. From what source was there an acknowledgment of the deity of Jesus?

MARK 3:11 _____

26. Did Jesus want such testimony to His deity?

MARK 3:12 _____

27. Where was Jesus when He called His disciples?

MARK 3:13 _____

28. What double purpose did Jesus have for them?

MARK 3:14 _____

29. What special detail is always given in connection with Judas?

MARK 3:19 _____

30. Should one who follows Jesus expect to sometimes be misunderstood by his friends?

MARK 3:21 _____

31. How did the scribes say that Jesus did His miracles?

MARK 3:22 _____

32. Why was their argument senseless?

MARK 3:23-26 _____

33. What did Jesus say about this sin of attributing His works to the power of the devil?

MARK 3:29 _____

The sin which has no forgiveness is not a common sin. Even atheists and infidels of today could scarcely come up to the degree of guilt of those who actually witnessed the works of Christ and then attributed them to a vile spirit.

34. Does Jesus promise to forgive and save all those who come to Him?

JOHN 6:37 _____

35. What did the people notice of which Jesus apparently took no notice?

MARK 3:32 _____

36. Whom did Jesus speak of here as being His mother and His brethren?

MARK 3:34, 35 _____

It is remarkable that in the two cases where the mother of Jesus figures in the story of His ministry, she appears in order to be reproved and to be placed, so far as relationship was concerned, on the same plane as all obedient servants of God.

check-up time No. 2

You have just studied some important truths about the beginning of the ministry of the Lord Jesus. Review your study by rereading the Scripture lesson, the questions and your written answers. If you aren't sure of an answer, reread the Scripture portion given to see if you can find the answer. Then take the following test to see how well you understand the important truths you have studied. This exam covers lesson 2.

In the right-hand margin write "True" or "False" after each of the following statements.

1. Jesus was impressed by the faith of the palsied man. _____

2. Forgiving the man's sins was more important than healing his body. _____

3. The physical healing was proof of Jesus' ability to forgive sins. _____

4. Jesus said fasting was of no value. _____

5. The Lord Jesus used Jonah as an illustration that the Sabbath was made for man. _____

6. There is such a thing as righteous anger. _____

7. The demons acknowledged that Jesus was God. _____

8. Judas is always identified as the traitor. _____

9. There is a sin which can never be forgiven. _____

10. Family relationships can keep one from doing God's will. _____

Turn to page 48 and check your answers.

God's Servant Works Miracles

MARK 4 AND 5

Chapter 4 gives the parable of the soils and records the miracle of the stilling of the storm . . .

1. What does the seed represent?

MARK 4:14 _____

2. How soon after the seed is planted does Satan make his counterattack?

MARK 4:15 _____

3. In the next class of hearers, why did the seed die so quickly?

MARK 4:5, 6 _____

4. What usually happens to those who mistake feelings for faith?

MARK 4:17 _____

Nothing shows more accurately how deeply a person has gone with God than afflictions and persecutions for the Word's sake.

5. Why didn't the seed sown on the third type of ground mature and bear fruit?

MARK 4:7 _____

6. What class of people did it represent?

MARK 4:18, 19 _____

7. What three different degrees of fertility are noted in the fourth sowing?

MARK 4:8 _____

8. What does this mean?

MARK 4:20 _____

9. What must be hidden from those who are not spiritually receptive?

MARK 4:11, 12 _____

Parables are here shown to be necessary in dealing with the mixed crowd following Jesus at that time. He could not confide His full mind to them, but He could set them thinking by parables. The detailed explanations were reserved for those who were spiritually prepared to receive them.

10. If we do not make good use of the knowledge we have, what will happen?

MARK 4:25 _____

Use or lose is a great principle.

11. If we plant gospel seed in true faith, what does God promise to do?

I CORINTHIANS 3:6, 7 _____

12. What happened at the close of the day after Jesus had given His disciples such wonderful teachings about faith?

MARK 4:35-38 _____

13. Had they really learned much about faith?

MARK 4:17, 38 _____

14. Although Jesus had been sleeping the sleep of human exhaustion, what did He do that proved His deity?

MARK 4:39 _____

15. What other tumults is Jesus able to calm?

John 14:27 _____

16. What fact about Jesus impressed His disciples now?

Mark 4:41 _____

Chapter 5 tells of the healing of the demoniac and the woman, and the raising of Jairus' daughter . . .

There seemed to be a peculiar outbreak from the kingdom of darkness at the time of Christ's advent, as if the forces of evil had been held in reserve for that critical time, then to make their fiercest assault. Hence we read of the most remarkable instances of demon possession.

17. What was the cause of this man's superhuman strength?

Mark 5:2 _____

18. What effect did the sight of Jesus have upon him?

Mark 5:6 _____

19. How did he know who Jesus was?

James 2:19 _____

20. What kind of tumult does Jesus here prove His power to calm?

Mark 5:8 _____

21. What habitation did the demons prefer to having none at all?

Mark 5:12 _____

22. How many pigs were drowned for the saving of a human soul?

Mark 5:13 _____

We need not feel sorry for the pigs, for they would have been butchered anyway. Perhaps the loss of the swine would remind the keeper that it was contrary to the law for Jews to keep swine. It served as an object lesson.

23. Did the people beseech Jesus to stay and heal their sick?

MARK 5:17 _____

24. What change is seen in the man's attitude toward Jesus?

MARK 5:18; cf. verse 7 _____

_____

25. What did Jesus ask the man to do?

MARK 5:19 _____

26. How was the woman's perfect faith in Christ revealed?

MARK 5:28 _____

27. How did Jesus discern this touch of true faith?

MARK 5:30 _____

The word "virtue" is used in the old medical sense. A physician speaks of the virtue of certain drugs, meaning their healing properties.

28. Why did Jesus ask who touched Him?

ROMANS 10:10 _____

29. After the messengers told Jairus of the death of his daughter, what did Jesus say to him?

MARK 5:36 _____

30. Although the child was dead as far as men were concerned, was she dead to Jesus?

MARK 5:39 _____

31. Did the fact that the girl was miraculously healed do away with the necessity for human care?

MARK 5:43 _____

32. What shows that Jesus did not work the miracle in order to win the admiration of the curious?

MARK 5:43 _____

God's Servant and the World

MARK 6

Chapter 6 records the death of John the Baptist and the feeding of the 5,000 . . .

1. Why didn't the people of Nazareth accept the wonderful wisdom and works of Jesus?

MARK 6:2, 3 _____

_____

2. If Jesus had worked miracles just to convince skeptics, where would He have done His mightiest works?

MARK 6:4, 5 _____

3. To whom were the twelve disciples sent at this time?

MATTHEW 10:5, 6 _____

4. What instructions show that He wanted them to be devoted wholly to the preaching of the Word, and to waste no time?

MARK 6:8, 9 _____

5. Were they to allow themselves to be discouraged if their message was not received?

MARK 6:11 _____

6. What did they call upon men to do?

MARK 6:12 _____

7. Whom did Herod think Jesus was?

MARK 6:14 _____

8. What was Herod's attitude toward the gospel John preached?

Mark 6:20 _____

9. Why did Herod have a fear of John's return?

Mark 6:16-28 _____

10. What was the greatest need of the multitudes who came to hear Christ?

Mark 6:34 _____

11. What did Jesus tell the disciples to do as a first step in feeding the people?

Mark 6:38 _____

We must not neglect the resources within our reach. If what we have is not working for God, it is of little use to ask Him to supply the needs. The workings of omnipotence are usually mingled with the gifts and labors of human hands.

12. What did Jesus do before distributing the food?

Mark 6:41 _____

13. Does Jesus want any of that which has been multiplied by His blessing to be wasted?

Mark 6:43 _____

14. What did Jesus always do after a great occasion?

Mark 6:46 _____

If Christian workers lack poise and power, it is because they do not pause for prayer and praise.

15. What happened as soon as Jesus stepped into the boat?

Mark 6:51 _____

16. What was the result in the disciples' hearts?

Mark 6:51, 52 _____

There can be no calm about us, no peace within us, and no progress for us until Jesus is aboard in our lives.

check-up time No. 3

You have just studied some important truths about the miracles of the Lord Jesus. Review your study by rereading the Scripture lesson, the questions and your written answers. If you aren't sure of an answer, reread the Scripture portion given to see if you can find the answer. Then take the following test to see how well you understand the important truths you have studied. This exam covers lessons 3 and 4.

Circle the letter beside the word which most accurately completes the sentence.

1. The seed represents (a) God, (b) people, (c) the Word.

2. The soils represent (a) actual ground, (b) different nationalities, (c) human hearts.

3. During the storm the disciples were (a) fearful, (b) trustful, (c) unconcerned.

4. Confession of Jesus' deity was made by (a) His disciples, (b) all the people, (c) demons.

5. After the healing of the demoniac, the people (a) begged Jesus to stay, (b) begged Jesus to leave, (c) were indifferent.

6. The healing of Jairus' daughter was (a) immediate, (b) gradual, (c) partial.

7. The twelve disciples were sent to preach to (a) Gentiles, (b) Jews, (c) everyone.

8. Jesus was unable to do miracles in Nazareth because of (a) unbelief, (b) disinterest, (c) persecution.

9. Herod thought Jesus was (a) a false prophet, (b) God, (c) John the Baptist.

10. Jesus went away to a mountain apart (a) to get some rest, (b) to visit with the disciples, (c) to pray.

Turn to page 48 and check your answers.

God's Servant Heals and Teaches

MARK 7 AND 8

Chapter 7 records the rebuke of the Pharisees and the answer to the Gentile woman . . .

1. What two groups now find fault with Jesus?

MARK 7:1 _____

2. Did they complain because the disciples did contrary to the law of God or contrary to tradition?

MARK 7:5 _____

The traditions were so-called inspired commentaries on the Old Testament law. The Rabbis had added to the simple distinctions between clean and unclean food, endless rites and ceremonies.

3. Who had foretold the time when the chosen people would care more for the external form than for the reality of God's Word?

MARK 7:6 _____

4. What example did Jesus use to show that these people gave more importance to tradition than to the Word of God?

MARK 7:10-12 _____

_____

5. What is the first thing Jesus mentions as being the fruit of a corrupt heart?

MARK 7:21 _____

6. What is the source of all defilement?

MARK 7:23 _____

7. What can be done with such a heart?

PSALM 51:10 _____

8. What seemingly harsh words did Jesus utter to the Gentile woman?

MARK 7:27 _____

_____

Note that the word for "dogs" is literally "little dogs" or "pet dogs," not the word often applied by Jews to Gentiles. Furthermore, much would depend upon the tone of Jesus' voice and the look in His eyes.

9. Who is the author of such faith as this woman showed?

HEBREWS 12:2 _____

Jesus was quickening and testing her faith. He knew that she would stand the test and have a purer faith than if she had received the blessing without a test.

10. What special commendation did she receive?

MATTHEW 15:28 _____

_____

11. What was the verdict of those who saw the miracle of the healing of the deaf and dumb man?

MARK 7:37 _____

Chapter 8 tells of the feeding of the 4,000 and records Peter's confession of faith . . .

12. What proof is there that Jesus was concerned with the physical as well as the spiritual needs of the people?

MARK 8:2 _____

_____

13. Had the previous feeding of the multitude made much of an impression on the disciples?

MARK 8:4 _____

14. How does Jesus show that they had something that needed to be yielded to Him to be used?

MARK 8:5 _____

15. What was the motive of the Pharisees in seeking signs?

MARK 8:11 _____

16. What was the final sign Jesus gave?

MATTHEW 12:39, 40 _____

17. What warning did Jesus give His disciples?

MARK 8:15 _____

The leaven of the Pharisees was formalism and the leaven of Herod was worldliness.

18. What could the blind man see after Jesus first touched his eyes?

MARK 8:24 _____

19. What was the result of Jesus' second touch?

MARK 8:25 _____

There is a special lesson intended in the incident viewed in connection with what follows. Perhaps, also, there was a special reason in relation to the individual. Dr. Parker says: "Some men cannot stand instantaneousness."

20. Who were men saying Jesus was?

MARK 8:28 _____

Now we have an illustration of the gradual opening of spiritual eyes. The disciples did not have spiritual sight to see the deity of Christ all at once.

21. What was Peter's full answer?

MATTHEW 16:16 _____

Jesus made this utterance the cornerstone of His church. He saw in it the germ of all that living faith by which true believers should always be animated.

22. For what purpose was the Scripture given?

JOHN 20:31 _____

_____

23. When Jesus speaks of His death, what does He always connect with it?

MARK 8:31 _____

24. To whom did Jesus attribute the suggestion that it was possible for Him to avoid the cross?

MARK 8:33 _____

25. In order to be a follower of Christ, what must one deny?

MARK 8:34 _____

26. What is implied in taking up His cross?

GALATIANS 6:14 _____

_____

To take up His cross means walking in fellowship with Him, involving one somewhat in the hostile treatment Jesus suffered.

27. Is all the pleasure of the world anything compared to the value of a soul?

MARK 8:36 _____

28. Why was Paul not ashamed of the gospel of Christ?

ROMANS 1:16 _____

29. What will be the price of being ashamed of Jesus and His words?

MARK 8:38 _____

_____

30. Will one who is a true believer be ashamed?

ROMANS 10:11 _____

check-up time No. 4

You have just studied some important truths about the ministry of the Lord Jesus. Review your study by rereading the Scripture lesson, the questions and your written answers. If you aren't sure of an answer, reread the Scripture portion given to see if you can find the answer. Then take the following test to see how well you understand the important truths you have studied. This exam covers lesson 5.

Circle the letter beside the word which most accurately completes the sentence.

1. The Pharisees were most concerned with keeping (a) God's Word, (b) Roman law, (c) their traditions.

2. In God's sight evil thoughts are (a) not as bad as murder, (b) worse than murder, (c) as sinful as murder.

3. When Jesus saw the hungry multitude, He (a) provided food for them, (b) sent them away, (c) told the disciples to feed them.

4. As a final sign Jesus used the experience of (a) Noah, (b) Jonah, (c) Daniel.

5. Teaching about the death of the Lord Jesus is always connected with (a) His resurrection, (b) the cross, (c) Judas.

6. The disciple who confessed that Jesus was God's Son was (a) James, (b) Peter, (c) John.

7. The Scripture was given primarily that we may (a) be wise, (b) live a good life, (c) know how to be saved.

8. In Romans Paul speaks of the gospel as being (a) interesting, (b) powerful, (c) profitable.

9. Jesus will be ashamed of those who (a) follow Him, (b) turn away from Him, (c) are ashamed of Him.

10. To follow Jesus one must deny (a) money, (b) family, (c) oneself.

Turn to page 48 and check your answers.

God's Servant Transfigured

MARK 9

Chapter 9 tells of the transfiguration of Jesus and of the powerlessness of the disciples . . .

The transfiguration shows that the death Jesus had foretold was not the result of weakness on His part, but the great purpose for which He had become incarnate. The word means a "complete and remarkable change," not merely outward, but a substantial inward change as well.

1. Who were the "some" who had the opportunity of seeing His kingdom come in power?

MARK 9:2 _____

2. When were the same three with Him again?

MARK 14:32, 33 _____

What they saw and heard on the mount should have helped them to understand what took place later in Gethsemane.

3. Who appeared with Jesus?

MARK 9:4 _____

4. What did they talk about?

LUKE 9:30, 31_____

5. What rash proposal did Peter make?

MARK 9:5 _____

6. What were God's last two words from heaven concerning His Son?

MARK 9:7 _____

7. How do we know that all this made a deep impression on Peter's mind?

II PETER 1:17, 18 _____

_____

8. How long were they to withhold the story of what had happened?

MARK 9:9 _____

9. What question troubled the disciples?

MARK 9:11 _____

_____

10. Who had already come in the spirit and power of Elias?

LUKE 1:13-17 _____

11. What was the cause of the excitement at the foot of the mount?

MARK 9:17, 18 _____

12. What word suggested the father's doubt?

MARK 9:22 _____

13. Where did Jesus put the "if"?

MARK 9:23 _____

14. What response did the father make?

MARK 9:24 _____

15. What did Jesus say was the reason for the disciples' lack of power?

MARK 9:29 _____

_____

16. What was the reaction of the disciples when Jesus told them what was going to happen to Him?

MARK 9:31, 32 _____

17. What did Jesus say one must do in order to be first?

MARK 9:35 _____

18. In order to receive a reward, how must one's service be done?

MARK 9:41 _____

19. Was Jesus here teaching literal multilation of the body?

MARK 9:43-45; GALATIANS 5:24 _____

_____

It is better to part with anything or everything than to go to hell where conscience preys as a worm upon the soul, and where unsatisfied passions burn on forever (LUKE 16:24, 25).

20. Does Jesus indicate that future punishment will sometime end?

MARK 9:48 _____

21. What means does God sometimes use to perfect His children?

I PETER 4:12-14 _____

22. What gives relish to everything in a Christian's life?

COLOSSIANS 4:6 _____

Insipid salt is another name for a savorless life. The grace of Christ communicates seasoning to a life that makes it different from any other life. The world despises a savorless Christian.

God's Servant Moves Toward Jerusalem

MARK 10

*Chapter 10 tells of the rich young ruler, the
dispute of the disciples, and the healing
of Bartimaeus . . .*

1. What question did Jesus give in reply to the Pharisees when they asked Him about divorce?

MARK 10:2, 3 _____

2. What word suggests that God tolerated divorce because of the sinful condition of men?

MARK 10:4, 5 _____

3. How close does God regard the union of husband and wife to be?

MARK 10:8 _____

4. Is it a serious thing for anyone to keep a child from coming to Christ?

MARK 10:14, 15 _____

5. What words indicate this?

MARK 10:14 _____

6. Was there any possibility that the rich young man had perfectly kept the law?

JAMES 2:10, 11 _____

7. What is the law intended to do?

ROMANS 3:19, 20; GALATIANS 3:24 _____

8. Was Jesus denying His deity in saying that absolute goodness is found only in God?

JOHN 10:30 _____

9. What action of Jesus shows that He recognized the young man's sincerity?

MARK 10:21 _____

10. What is the real danger in the possession of much money?

MARK 10:24 _____

11. Who alone can work the miracle of making a rich man "poor in spirit" so that he will want to be saved?

MARK 10:27 _____

12. What was going to happen to Jesus in Jerusalem?

MARK 10:33 _____

13. What statement of Jesus should have reassured the disciples that He was not going to be simply the victim of circumstances?

MARK 10:34 _____

14. What did James and John want for themselves?

MARK 10:37 _____

15. Who was the first martyr among the Twelve?

ACTS 12:1, 2 _____

16. What is the way of attaining heaven's highest honors?

MARK 10:44 _____

17. What was the first object of Christ's earthly life?

MARK 10:45 _____

18. What action of Bartimaeus shows his zeal to get to Jesus?
Mark 10:50 _____

check-up time No. 5

You have just studied some important truths about the Lord Jesus. Review your study by rereading the Scripture lesson, the questions and your written answers. If you aren't sure of an answer, reread the Scripture portion given to see if you can find the answer. Then take the following test to see how well you understand the important truths you have studied. This exam covers lessons 6 and 7.

In the right-hand margin write "True" or "False" after each of the following statements.

1. Peter, James and John saw the transfiguration of the Lord Jesus. _____

2. The disciples failed to recognize the two men who appeared and talked with Jesus. _____

3. Peter soon forgot this experience. _____

4. Jesus was referring to John the Baptist when He spoke of Elias. _____

5. Children are important in God's sight. _____

6. The rich young ruler was just a hypocrite. _____

7. Jesus taught that only rich persons could be saved. _____

8. The disciples failed to understand when Jesus told them of His death. _____

9. Peter was the first of the disciples to die for Christ. _____

10. Bartimaeus wasn't sure Jesus could heal him. _____

Turn to page 48 and check your answers.

God's Servant Revealed as King

MARK 11 AND 12

Chapter 11 gives details of the triumphal entry . . .

We have here the account of how Christ planned the lowliest of all memorable parades. The very style in which Jesus made this entry should have proved to every reflective spectator that He had no intention at that time of acting the part of an earthly monarch.

1. Why should the people have recognized the manner in which Jesus entered Jerusalem?

ZECHARIAH 9:9 ⎯⎯⎯⎯⎯⎯⎯⎯⎯⎯⎯⎯⎯⎯⎯⎯

2. On what will Jesus ride when He returns as King?

REVELATION 19:11 ⎯⎯⎯⎯⎯⎯⎯⎯⎯⎯⎯⎯⎯⎯

3. Why were the owners of the colt willing to let it go?

MARK 11:3-6 ⎯⎯⎯⎯⎯⎯⎯⎯⎯⎯⎯⎯⎯⎯⎯

4. What was done to the colt before Jesus sat upon it?

MARK 11:7 ⎯⎯⎯⎯⎯⎯⎯⎯⎯⎯⎯⎯⎯⎯⎯⎯

5. Why did the people cry out?

MARK 11:9 ⎯⎯⎯⎯⎯⎯⎯⎯⎯⎯⎯⎯⎯⎯⎯⎯

6. What kingdom did the people think was about to be set up?

MARK 11:10 ⎯⎯⎯⎯⎯⎯⎯⎯⎯⎯⎯⎯⎯⎯⎯

7. Should they have expected an earthly kingdom at this time?

ZECHARIAH 9:9 ⎯⎯⎯⎯⎯⎯⎯⎯⎯⎯⎯⎯⎯⎯

8. What suggested that there should have been fruit on the fig tree?

MARK 11:13 _____

The figs usually appear before the leaves, hence, although it was not the time for either fruit or foliage, expectations would be raised on seeing the green leaves. This was a freak tree, an illustration of those who make great religious profession in season and out of season, and yet are without fruit. Jesus' many miracles were miracles of mercy. A useless tree is the only thing cursed.

9. For what is God's house to be noted?

MARK 11:17 _____

10. How complete was the miracle upon the fig tree?

MARK 11:20 _____

11. What lesson did Jesus immediately suggest?

MARK 11:22, 23 _____

_____

12. Is it possible for any Christian to bear fruit apart from faith? Explain.

HEBREWS 11:6 _____

13. Who is the author of true faith?

HEBREWS 12:2 _____

14. Why were the scribes and Pharisees unable to answer the question Jesus asked?

MARK 11:29-33 _____

Chapter 12 deals with the parable of the vineyard and the question of the resurrection . . .

15. Why would the Jews so well understand the parable of the vineyard?

ISAIAH 5:1-7 _____

_____

This parable is an Old Testament theme which is almost exactly repeated in Jesus' discourse.

16. What did Israel do to the prophets whom God sent to demand fruit?

MATTHEW 23:29-32 _____

17. What happened in "the fullness of time"?

GALATIANS 4:4 _____

18. What will be the fate of those who reject the heir?

MARK 12:9 _____

19. Who later made use of the scripture which Jesus quotes from

Psalm 118?

ACTS 4:10, 11; I PETER 2:7 _____

The psalmist is said to have referred to an actual incident in the rebuilding of the temple. A stone which the builders had rejected proved to be of such excellent quality that it was used for the cornice. The Jews had always understood this as referring to their Messiah.

20. What was the next catch question that was asked?

MARK 12:14 _____

21. What did Jesus' answer indicate about tax money?

MARK 12:17 _____

22. What example did the Sadducees give in an attempt to make the doctrine of the resurrection look ridiculous?

MARK 12:20-23 _____

_____

23. How did Jesus look upon this question?

MARK 12:24 _____

24. How did God refer to Himself in their own Scriptures?

Mark 12:26, 27 _____

25. What was the sincere question of the scribe?

Mark 12:28 _____

The Rabbis counted 613 precepts, divided into "weighty" and "light."
There were 248 affirmative and 365 negative laws. It was argued that
of such a number, all could not be of the same value.

26. What infallible answer did Jesus deliver in one sentence?

Mark 12:30 _____

_____

27. What law did Jesus name as second in importance?

Mark 12:31 _____

28. Against whom did Jesus then warn the people?

Mark 12:38-40 _____

29. Why did the widow's very small gift make a greater impression on Jesus than any other?

Mark 12:44 _____

God's Servant Foretells the Future

MARK 13

Chapter 13 gives the Olivet Discourse . . .

1. What impressed the disciples as they were leaving the temple?

MARK 13:1 _____

2. What seemingly improbable prophecy did Jesus make?

MARK 13:2 _____

Our Lord's prediction is more remarkable when it is known that there were stones of white marble 67 feet long, seven feet high and nine feet wide. Josephus tells us that Titus held a council of generals and decided to save the temple as an ornament to the Empire, but for some reason the soldiers disregarded. One greater than Titus had decreed that it should come down.

3. What was the opening warning of the prophetic discourse?

MARK 13:5 _____

4. What would characterize the entire age?

MARK 13:7 _____

5. What would happen to followers of Christ when war came?

MARK 13:9 _____

6. What did Daniel prophesy would take place after the cutting off of the Messiah?

DANIEL 9:26 _____

7. When was the desolation of the temple accomplished?

LUKE 21:20, 21 _____

Josephus tells us that the Romans brought their standards into the temple and offered sacrifices to them. Bear in mind that there is a double fulfillment of these things, for the prophecies show a future gathering of armies about Jerusalem under antichrist.

8. What will happen at the close of the great tribulation described here which Matthew's account shows is future?

MATTHEW 24:29, 30 _____

_____

9. What should a Christian remember when he hears reports of miracle workers and Messiahs?

MARK 13:21-23 _____

10. Will the second coming of Christ be an historical event as His first coming was?

MARK 13:26 _____

11. What will happen in connection with His coming?

MARK 13:27 _____

12. What symbol in addition to the fig tree did Jesus use in speaking of Israel?

MARK 12:1 _____

13. What is the significance of Israel's gathering together after her long dispersion?

MARK 13:29 _____

14. Who alone knows the exact time of the second coming?

MARK 13:32 _____

15. What is to be our chief concern while we wait for His return?

MARK 13:35-37 _____

check-up time No. 6

You have just studied some important truths about Jesus' teaching. Review your study by rereading the Scripture lesson, the questions and your answers. If you aren't sure of an answer, reread the Scripture portion given to see if you can find the answer. Then take the following test to see how well you understand the important truths you have studied. This exam covers lessons 8 and 9.

In the right-hand margin write "True" or "False" after each of the following statements.

1. Jesus' entry into Jerusalem was proof that He was planning to set up an earthly kingdom immediately.　———————

2. Nobody noticed Him entering the city.　———————

3. God's house is to be a house of prayer.　———————

4. The nation of Israel was compared to the fig tree.　———————

5. The Sadducees believed in the resurrection.　———————

6. The most important commandment is to love God.　———————

7. Daniel had foretold the destruction of the temple.　———————

8. The regathering of Israel as a nation is of great importance.　———————

9. We can be sure that Christ will return.　———————

10. It matters greatly what we do during His absence.　———————

Turn to page 48 and check your answers.

God's Servant Refused

MARK 14

Chapter 14 tells of Jesus' agony in the Garden and of His arrest . . .

1. Who was the woman who anointed Jesus at this time?

JOHN 12:2, 3 _____

2. Who first suggested the wastefulness of this act?

JOHN 12:4, 5 _____

3. For what purpose did Jesus say the ointment had been given?

MARK 14:7, 8 _____

4. What memorial was erected to this woman's gift?

MARK 14:9 _____

_____

This was a bold thing for one to promise, and yet the word of Jesus has been fulfilled for these 1900 years. Only He who was the eternal Son could pledge the immortality of this woman's act.

5. How much money was Judas willing to take to betray Jesus?

MATTHEW 26:15 _____

6. What did Jesus tell His disciples to prepare?

MARK 14:12-16 _____

7. What strange utterance of Jesus disturbed the disciples as they ate?

MARK 14:18 _____

8. What did they ask Him?

MATTHEW 26:22 _____

9. Does Jesus indicate that there would be hope for Judas' salvation sometime in the future?

MARK 14:21 _____

10. What do the wine and the bread symbolize?

I CORINTHIANS 11:24-26 _____

_____

11. What did Jesus say would be the attitude of the disciples that night?

MARK 14:27 _____

12. Who insisted that he would always remain true?

MARK 14:29 _____

13. Who were with Jesus in the Garden?

MARK 14:33 _____

14. What did Jesus pray?

MARK 14:36 _____

_____

15. What shows the great agony of spirit Jesus was enduring?

LUKE 22:44 _____

16. What were the disciples doing during this time?

MARK 14:37 _____

17. Did they need to pray for Jesus or for themselves?

MARK 14:38 _____

18. By what title did Judas address Jesus?

MARK 14:45 _____

19. Does the account of the young man slipping out of the linen cloth have any bearing on the story?

MARK 14:51, 52 _____

Tradition says this was Mark, then a young man. Like many other small details in the account, it shows the story is drawn from real life. We can understand how Mark, when writing this part of the story, would recall this detail.

20. Where was Peter at this point of the story?

MARK 14:54 _____

21. Did Jesus answer the false charges against Him?

MARK 14:60, 61 _____

22. Did He reply when they questioned His deity?

MARK 14:61, 62 _____

23. How did Peter begin to fulfill Christ's words to him?

MARK 14:68 _____

24. Why was there such a difference between Peter and Judas in this matter?

MARK 14:72; MATTHEW 27:5 _____

_____

God's Servant Crucified

MARK 15

Chapter 15 tells of the death and burial of the Lord Jesus . . .

1. What did Pilate ask Jesus?

MARK 15:2 _____

2. What was the custom in honor of the Jewish feast?

MARK 15:6 _____

3. Who suggested that Barabbas, the noted criminal, be released?

MARK 15:11 _____

4. Could the religious leaders answer Pilate's question?

MARK 15:14 _____

5. How did the soldiers mock the Lord Jesus?

MARK 15:17-19 _____

_____

6. Who helped carry the cross?

MARK 15:21 _____

7. What does "Golgotha" mean?

MARK 15:22 _____

8. Why didn't Jesus accept the drink offered to Him?

MARK 15:23 _____

9. What was significant about the soldiers' actions in verse 24?

PSALM 22:18 _____

_____

10. At what hour was Jesus nailed to the cross?

MARK 15:25 _____

11. At what hour did He die?

MARK 15:34 _____

12. Could Jesus have saved Himself and sinners at the same time?

MARK 15:31 _____

13. What agony climaxed the awful sufferings of Jesus?

MARK 15:34 _____

14. Why did God the Father turn from the Lord Jesus?

HABAKKUK 1:13; II CORINTHIANS 5:21 _____

_____

15. What victorious shout did Christ give?

JOHN 19:30 _____

16. Who took Jesus' life from Him?

JOHN 10:18 _____

17. What was the significance of the rent veil?

HEBREWS 9:6-8; 10:19, 20 _____

_____

18. Who asked for the body of Jesus?

MARK 15:43 _____

19. Who waited to the very end to see where the body of Jesus was laid?

MARK 15:47 _____

check-up time No. 7

You have just studied some important truths about Jesus' death. Now take the following test to see how well you understand the important truths you have studied. This exam covers lessons 10 and 11.

Circle the letter beside the word or words which most accurately complete the sentence.

1. The woman who anointed Jesus was (a) Mary, His mother, (b) Mary Magdalene, (c) Mary of Bethany.

2. Jesus said He would be betrayed by (a) one of His disciples, (b) the people, (c) the Pharisees.

3. The disciple who most strongly insisted he would never desert Jesus was (a) John, (b) Matthew, (c) Peter.

4. While Jesus prayed in the Garden, the disciples (a) watched for the soldiers, (b) slept, (c) prayed.

5. Those responsible for the release of Barabbas were (a) the soldiers, (b) the people, (c) the chief priests.

6. The crown of thorns was put on Jesus by (a) Pilate, (b) the Jewish rulers, (c) the soldiers.

7. Christ died at (a) the sixth hour, (b) the ninth hour, (c) the twelfth hour.

8. The parting of Jesus' clothes was the fulfillment of a prophecy in (a) Isaiah, (b) Zechariah, (c) Psalms.

9. The greatest agony the Lord Jesus endured was (a) the physical suffering, (b) the betrayal by Judas, (c) God's turning from Him.

10. The man who asked for the body of Jesus was (a) Zacchaeus, (b) Joseph of Arimathea, (c) Nicodemus.

Turn to page 48 and check your answers.

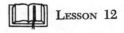

God's Servant Triumphant

MARK 16

Chapter 16 gives the account of the resurrection and ascension . . .

1. If the women had really understood what Jesus had taught, would they have gone to the tomb with spices?

MARK 16:1 _____

2. On what day was Jesus raised from the dead?

MARK 16:2 _____

It is sometimes said that there is no New Testament command for the Lord's Day taking the place of the Mosaic Sabbath. There was no need of words to enact the change for it was legislated into practice by divine action. The resurrection of the world's Saviour speaks louder than any words.

3. Had the stone been rolled away to let Jesus out or to let the women see in?

MATTHEW 28:2 _____

4. What had Jesus said about Himself that was proved by the resurrection?

ROMANS 1:4 _____

5. Who was to be given a special message?

MARK 16:7 _____

6. Where had Jesus said He would meet His disciples?

MARK 16:7; cf. 14:28 _____

7. What did the excited women do?

MARK 16:8 _____

_____

8. To whom did they first tell the news?

JOHN 20:2 _____ .

9. By whom was Jesus seen first?

MARK 16:9 _____

10. In what state were Jesus' followers before they heard the news?

MARK 16:10 _____

11. What was their reaction to Mary Magdalene's words?

MARK 16:11 _____

What becomes of the modern theory that Jesus' disciples had worked themselves up into such a fever of expectation that the wish was father to the thought? The record tells us that they were not in a frame of mind to believe it and did not until they were shown.

12. Who tells the story of what took place between Jesus and the two with whom He walked?

LUKE 24:13-35 _____

13. To whom did Jesus later appear?

MARK 16:14 _____

14. What great commission did the risen Saviour give?

MARK 16:15 _____

_____

15. What command is linked with a true acceptance of Christ?

MARK 16:16 _____

16. What does the outward rite of baptism symbolize?

ROMANS 6:4, 5 _____

17. Why were signs necessary before the completion of the written Word?

MARK 16:17-20 _____

_____

Remember that Christianity was going forth alone in the hands of a few humble fishermen to grapple with systems which had held sway over the world for centuries.

18. How long was Jesus with His disciples after the resurrection?

ACTS 1:3 _____

19. In what words is the wonderful event of the ascension recorded?

MARK 16:19 _____

_____

20. What is Jesus doing for us now at the right hand of God?

HEBREWS 4:14-16; 7:25 _____

_____

check-up time No. 8

You have just studied some important truths about the resurrection of the Lord Jesus. Review your study by rereading the Scripture lesson, the questions and your written answers. If you aren't sure of an answer, reread the Scripture portion given to see if you can find the answer. Then take the following test to see how well you understand the important truths you have studied. This exam covers lesson 12.

In the right-hand margin write "True" or "False" after each of the following statements.

1. The disciples expected Jesus to rise from the dead. _____

2. Jesus rose from the tomb on the Jewish Sabbath. _____

3. The resurrection is vitally important to Christianity. _____

4. Peter was to be especially notified of what had happened. _____

5. The women immediately told the news to everyone they met. _____

6. Jesus was seen by His mother first. _____

7. Jesus gave His followers work to do. _____

8. Miraculous signs were to be the proof of God's power working in the disciples. _____

9. Jesus was with His disciples for forty days after His resurrection. _____

10. Jesus was taken up into heaven. _____

Turn to page 48 and check your answers.

Suggestions for class use

1. The class teacher may wish to tear this page from each workbook as the answer key is on the reverse side.

2. The teacher should study the lesson first, filling in the blanks in the workbook. He should be prepared to give help to the class on some of the harder places in the lesson. He should also take the self-check tests himself, check his answers with the answer key and look up any question answered incorrectly.

3. Class sessions can be supplemented by the teacher's giving a talk or leading a discussion on the subject to be studied. The class could then fill in the workbook together as a group, in teams, or individually. If so desired by the teacher, however, this could be done at home. The self-check tests can be done as homework by the class.

4. The self-check tests can be corrected at the beginning of each class session. A brief discussion of the answers can serve as review for the previous lesson.

5. The teacher should motivate and encourage his students. Some public recognition might well be given to class members who successfully complete this course.

answer key
to self-check tests

Be sure to look up any questions you answered incorrectly.

A gives the correct *answer*.

L gives the correct *lesson*.

R *refers* you back to the number of the question in the lesson itself, where the correct answer is to be found.

In each case, the test number and the lesson number are the same.

	TEST 1			TEST 2			TEST 3			TEST 4		
Question	A	L	R	A	L	R	A	L	R	A	L	R
1	T	1	3	F	2	1	c	3	1	c	5	2
2	F	1	2	T	2	2	c	3	2	c	5	5
3	T	1	3	T	2	6	a	3	13	a	5	14
4	F	1	7	F	2	13	c	3	19	b	5	16
5	T	1	4	F	2	16	b	3	23	a	5	23
6	F	1	10	T	2	21	a	3	31	b	5	21
7	T	1	15	T	2	25	b	4	3	c	5	22
8	T	1	21	T	2	29	a	4	2	b	5	28
9	T	1	26	T	2	33	c	4	7	c	5	29
10	F	1	29	T	2	36	c	4	14	c	5	25

	TEST 5			TEST 6			TEST 7			TEST 8		
Question	A	L	R	A	L	R	A	L	R	A	L	R
1	T	6	1	F	8	1	c	10	1	F	12	10
2	F	6	5	F	8	5	a	10	7	F	12	2
3	F	6	7	T	8	9	c	10	12	T	12	4
4	T	6	10	T	9	12	b	10	16	T	12	5
5	T	7	4	F	8	22	c	11	3	F	12	7
6	F	7	9	T	8	26	c	11	5	F	12	9
7	F	7	11	T	9	6	b	11	11	T	12	14
8	T	6	16	T	9	13	c	11	9	T	12	17
9	F	7	15	T	9	10	c	11	13	T	12	18
10	F	7	18	T	9	15	b	11	18	T	12	19

How well did you do?

0-1 wrong answers—excellent work

2-3 wrong answers—review errors carefully

4 or more wrong answers—restudy the lesson before going on to the next one